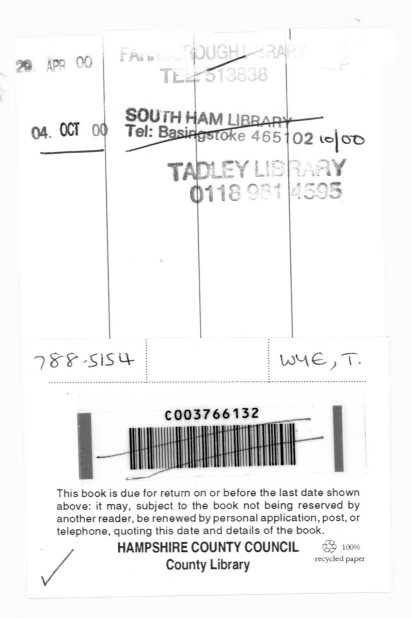
✱ PLEASE CHECK FOR BOOKLET AT BACK

D1436519

A COUPERIN ALBUM

ARRANGED BY TREVOR WYE

for flute and keyboard

GRADE III – VI

NOA

NOVELLO PUBLISHING LIMITED
8/9 Frith Street, London W1V 5TZ

Order No: NOV 120609

7.95

PREFACE

François Couperin, born in France in 1668, was often known as Couperin le Grand to distinguish him from his uncle and son who were also musicians. He lived during a great age in the development of musical style, to which he was particularly well positioned and qualified to contribute, holding several appointments at the Court of the Sun King, Louis XIV, in Paris and being a musician of genius.

Most of this collection is taken from Couperin's harpsichord works. The harpsichord is an instrument on which the player cannot vary the loudness of notes as he strikes them, and therefore uses ornaments and rhythmic movement to create 'expression'. Avoid therefore any stiffness of tempo. As Couperin himself said: 'It is better and more seemly not to beat time with the head, the body nor with the feet. One should have an air of ease . . .'

Three years before his death, he wrote: 'As scarcely anyone has composed more than I have in various styles, I hope that my family will discover in my (music) portfolios something which may cause me to be regretted, if indeed regrets are of any use to us after life.' He was no purist as far as choice of instrument or arrangement were concerned. A writer wrote in 1733 that Couperin's music was 'filled with excellent harmony, and having a noble and gracious melody'. He also mentioned that it could be played equally well on the violin or flute.

Couperin died on 12 September 1733.

Some ornaments have been removed and some changed, to create clearer understanding. An explanation of these can be found below. Some ornaments are in brackets. These are optional, though the piece will sound better if they *are* played.

To the Performer

The ornaments: Don't be put off by them. The most often asked question is: 'Why didn't the composer write . . . instead of . . .?' The answer is simple: it's *how* you play these two ornamental notes and not the value of them which is important. Composers decorated their music in the 18th century in the same way as they decorated their furniture and their clothes. In the case of the APPOGGIATURA written and played the way in which it was written indicated that the G was stressed and not the F sharp. The G should be louder and the F sharp played softly.

Most TRILLS start with an appoggiatura on the upper note which is stressed in the same way so that the trill itself is less loud.

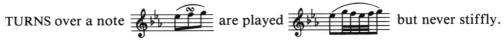

TURNS over a note are played but never stiffly.

You will also find MORDENTS both normal and INVERTED. The most common is though this is generally played starting with an upper note appoggiatura and is therefore played . When INVERTED it has a line through it played . In all mordents, be sure that the first note is *on* the beat.

I have replaced some of the original trills with mordents; experiment with this music and add mordents and trills if you feel it improves the character of the music. The appoggiaturas, of all the ornaments, create a sighing, restless and often sad quality to slow tunes. If this is what happens when *you* play them, then you've made a good start in understanding this style of playing.

T.W. 1986

The separate flute part is inserted.

CONTENTS

for Rachel Brown

A COUPERIN ALBUM

Piano accompaniments by
ROBERT SCOTT

Arranged by
TREVOR WYE

1. LA NOBLE FIERTÉ
NOBLE PRIDE

Cat. No. 12 0609

4

2. GAVOTTE

3. LA MORINETE*

4. CANARIES*

*A Spanish dance originally of the sixteenth century.

DOUBLE* DE CANARIES

Double: a variation on the preceding.

5. FORLANE*

*Forlane: an Italian dance, a favourite of the Venetian gondoliers.

RONDEAU

2me COUPLET

14

6. LA BANDOLINE*

*Bandoline: hair-setting lotion! Couperin was possibly thinking of a particular lady who used it.

7. LES ROZEAUX
WATER REEDS

[RONDEAU]

2me COUPLET

[RONDEAU

8. SOEUR MONIQUE*
SISTER MONIQUE

Possibly a portrait of a nun of Couperin's acquaintance.

9. L'ESPAGNOLÈTE*

Allegro moderato ♩. = 50

*The title could refer to a young Spanish girl.

10. JUGGLERS, ACROBATS, AND SHOWMEN, WITH BEARS AND MONKEYS

11. LA DOUCE ET PIQUANTE
SWEET AND SOUR

28

12. LES CALOTINS ET LES CALOTINES*

Play sections A-A-B-A-C-C-D-A

*This title refers to a play which appeared in Paris in 1721.

13. LES PAPILLONS
BUTTERFLIES

32

14. LE ROSSIGNOL-EN-AMOUR*
THE NIGHTINGALE IN LOVE

not necessary to stick too precisely to the beat in the Double (above). One must sacrifice all to taste, to the neatness of the passage work, and one must soften well the marked by mordents (♫) . . . . François Couperin.

Accens plaintifs

accel. e cresc.

Augmentés, par gradations imperceptibles

(Double du Rossignol)

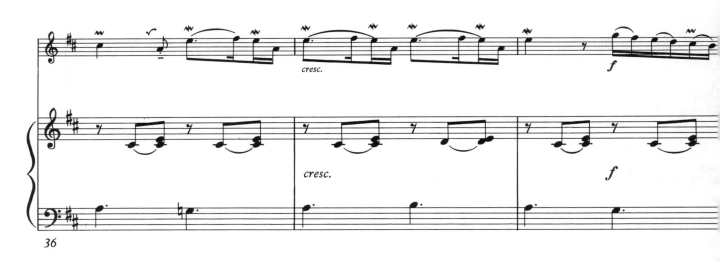

Printed and bound in Great Britain by
Caligraving Limited Thetford Norfolk